Paddy MacTaddy & the Dreadful Journey

by Mick Gowar

illustrated by
Marc Vyvyan-Jones

In a little village called Dunhooly, in the South of Ireland,
there lived six friends who loved making music together.
They called themselves *Paddy MacTaddy's Tipperary Showband*.
The members of the band were:

Fingal O'Tom-Tom, big and strong, who was the captain of
the Dunhooly hurling team and played the drums.

Dingle O'Plectrum – pheasant poacher, salmon stealer, trout tickler . . . and Country & Western-style guitar picker.

Bridie McBow, who was shaped like a cello but played the flute and the piccolo.

The twins, Jon-Jo and Finbow Costello, who played the piano –
Jon-Jo the left-hand bits, Finbow the right

and Paddy MacTaddy who drove the car that took them to the parties and dances where they played, and was the conductor.

And they all lived in the little village of Dunhooly, in County Ceilidh.

Well now, one Tuesday, Paddy MacTaddy
received a letter which said:

"We're having a dance next Saturday
in County Killkenny. Will you play?
(Enclosed is a map to show you the way.)"

So Paddy wrote back:
"Okay. We'll be there by eight –
we'll follow the map.
And don't worry, we're *never* late."

6

And he called a band practice for the very next day,
and the band sounded . . . *terrible*!

But Paddy and Bridie and Fingal and Dingle
and Jon-Jo and Finbow weren't too worried. They all agreed:
"We'll be alright on the night!"

So, on that Saturday they ate a big supper of
bacon and beans and baked potatoes
(so they wouldn't get hungry on the journey),
loaded all their instruments into Paddy's car
and set off on the road to Killkenny.

But they hadn't been driving
more than a couple of miles, when:

"Oh, no!" cried Paddy MacTaddy. "It's a puncture!"
But just because they had a puncture
did they give up?

– NO!

"Leave it to us!" shouted Fingal and Dingle.
And Fingal jacked up the car with his hurley-stick,
while Dingle undid all the nuts and changed the wheel.

Paddy MacCaddy
Buíon Ceoil (Showband)
Weddings – Dances – Wakes

Petrol

Paddy MacTaddy checked the time on his
old, gold watch: a quarter to eight!
But Paddy and Bridie and Fingal and Dingle
and Jon-Jo and Finbow weren't too worried. They all agreed:
"We'll be there in plenty of time."
So they ate the corned beef sandwiches they'd brought
(so they wouldn't get hungry on the journey)
and set off again on the road to Killkenny.

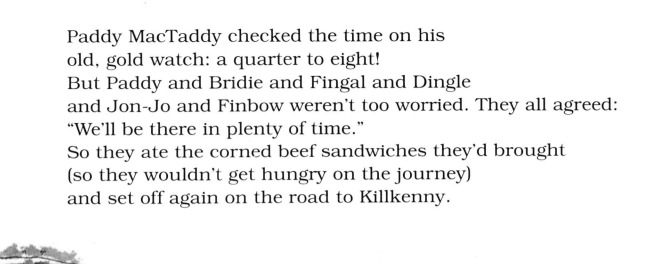

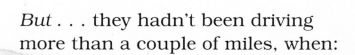

But . . . they hadn't been driving
more than a couple of miles, when:

The car stopped.
"We're out of petrol," said Paddy MacTaddy.
So he took the spare can of petrol out of the boot
and started to fill the tank:

"Oh, no!" cried Paddy MacTaddy. "The tank's full of holes
and all the petrol's dripping out!"
But just because the petrol tank was full of holes
and all the petrol was dripping out,
did they give up?

13

– NO!

"Leave it to us!" shouted Jon-Jo and Finbow.
And they plugged all the holes in the tank with their fingers –
Jon-Jo plugged the holes on the left, Finbow the right.

Paddy MacTaddy checked the time on his
old, gold watch: a quarter past eight!
But Paddy and Bridie and Fingal and Dingle
and Jon-Jo and Finbow weren't too worried. They all agreed:
"We'll be there in time for the interval."
So they ate the packet of chocolate biscuits they'd brought
(so they wouldn't get hungry on the journey)
and set off again on the road to Killkenny.

But . . . they hadn't been driving
more than a couple of miles, when:

"Oh, no!" cried Paddy MacTaddy. "The radiator's leaking,
the engine's overheating, and the exhaust pipe's fallen off!"
But just because the radiator was leaking,
the engine was overheating,
and the exhaust pipe had fallen off,
did they give up?

– NO!

"Leave it to me!" shouted Bridie.
And she mended the broken radiator with her piccolo
and replaced the exhaust pipe with her flute.

Paddy MacTaddy checked the time on his
old, gold watch: a quarter to nine!

But Paddy and Bridie and Fingal and Dingle
and Jon-Jo and Finbow weren't too worried. They all agreed:
"We'll be there in time to play the encore."
So they ate the packet of fruit gums they'd brought
(so they wouldn't get hungry on the journey)
and set off again on the road to Killkenny.

But . . . they hadn't been driving
more than a couple of miles, when:

"Oh, no!" cried Paddy MacTaddy. "The steering wheel's come off in my hand!"

This time, Paddy and Bridie and Fingal and Dingle and Jon-Jo and Finbow were *very* worried.
"Help! Help!"
they yelled, as the car hurtled down the hill

and into a ditch:

Nee-Naw Nee-Naw Nee-Naw Nee-Naw Nee-Naw!

The ambulance took them to
The Killkenny County Hospital,
where their broken legs were put
in plaster and their cuts and
bruises were bandaged.
But just because they were
in hospital with their legs
in plaster,
did they give up?

Ambulance

– NO!

"I know !" cried Paddy MacTaddy. "We'll do the show *right here*!"
So Paddy and Bridie and Fingal and Dingle
and Jon-Jo and Finbow sang a song
all about their journey from Dunhooly to Killkenny.

And they all agreed: "It'll be a hit record!"

And for once, they were right!

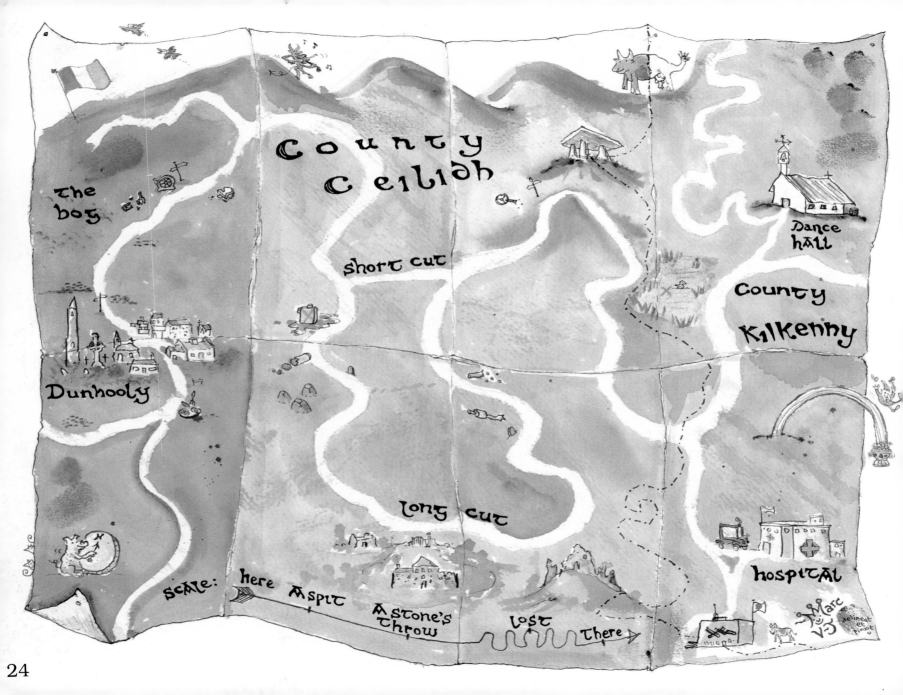

County Ceilidh

the bog

short cut

Dunhooly

long cut

Dance hall

County Kilkenny

hospital

SCALE: here A spit A stone's throw lost there

Marc V5

24